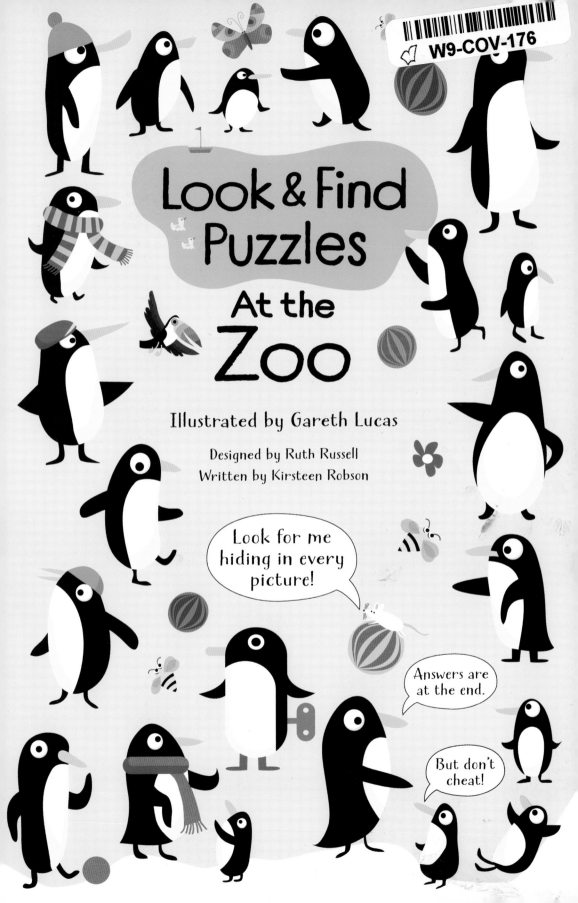

Can you find...   another 2 eggs like this   3 more baby ostriches

2

Can you find... 1 more ice-cream cone another one of these

3

another can
of blue paint

1 paintbrush
like this one

2 more
pink gloves

Look for two striped hoops.

Who's got a seashell necklace?

Can you find...

3 more purple crowns

2 different beach balls

Spot two hotdogs.

Can you find my pink fishing net?

Can you find... another duck 5 butterflies like this one

Who's riding on a blue scooter?

Which other two animals have hats?

Can you find...   3 more orange fish   4 other pink birds

12

Spot a bear with a snowball.

Find another bear just like me!

Can you find...

2 more robins like this

another 2 ice-skates

Can you
see three baby
owls?

Find three
popcorn
pieces.

Can you find...   2 other
squirrels

another
holly leaf

14

Can you find...

1 more fish like this

another pair of sunglasses

Who has a hat AND a scarf?

Can you see a snowboarder?

Can you find...

2 different toy boats

this purple penguin's twin

18

Where's y rubber ring?

3 more ducklings

another wind-up toy

5 more wasps

19

Can you find...   another 3   5 more scissors
green fish   like these

Can you find... another snail, just the same 5 more red spotted bugs

Please help me find my teddy bear!

Can you see two donkeys?

Can you find... another red camera — 3 more blue birds

24

25

Look for two camels with blankets.

Can you spot another green frog?

Can you find...

3 other blue beetles

2 more snakes

26

5 different
plant pots

another bird
like this

1 more
purple tail

Answers

Cover

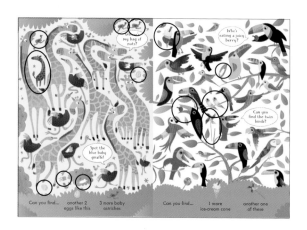

2–3

4–5

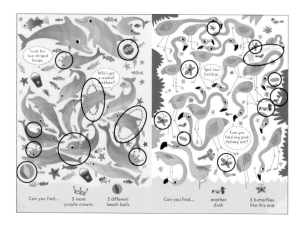

6–7

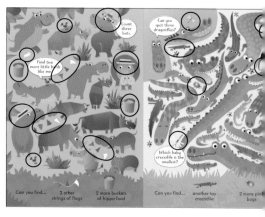

8–9

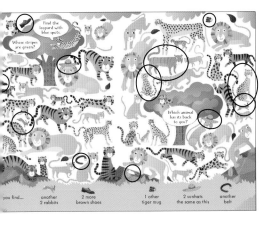

10-11

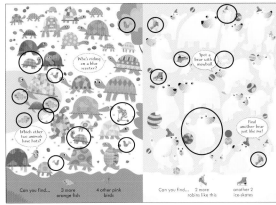

12-13

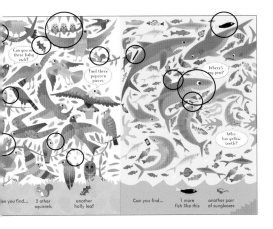

14-15

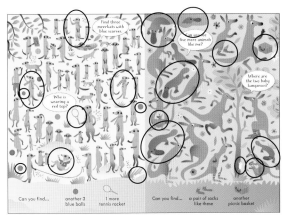

16-17

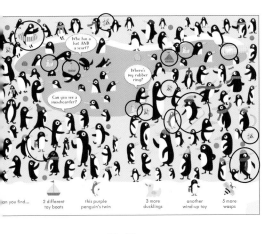

18-19

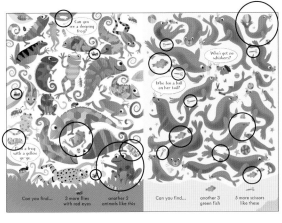

20-21

31

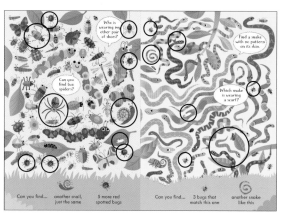

22-23

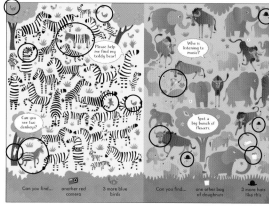

24-25

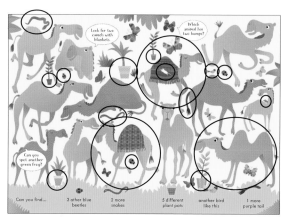

26-27

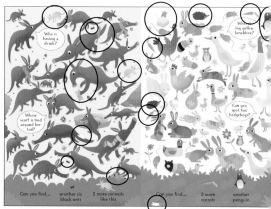

28-29

First published in 2021 by Usborne Publishing Ltd, Usborne House, 83-85 Saffron Hill, London, EC1N 8RT, England. usborne.com ©2021 Usborne Publishing Ltd. The name Usborne and the Balloon logo are trade marks of Usborne Publishing Ltd. All rights reserved. No part of this publication may be reproduced, stored in a retrieval system, or transmitted in any form or by any means, electronic, mechanical, photocopying, recording or otherwise without the prior permission of Usborne Publishing Ltd. First published in America in 2021, UE, EDC, Tulsa, Oklahoma 74146, usbornebooksandmore.com Printed in China.